THE REVENGE
OF THE BABY-SAT

THE REVENGE OF THE BABY-SAT

A Calvin and Hobbes Collection by Bill Watterson

Andrews McMeel
Publishing®

Kansas City · Sydney · London

Calvin and Hobbes is distributed internationally by Universal Uclick.

The Revenge of the Baby-Sat copyright © 1991 by Bill Watterson. All rights reserved. Printed in China. No part of this book may be used or reproduced in any manner whatsoever without written permission except in the case of reprints in the context of reviews.

Andrews McMeel Publishing, LLC
an Andrews McMeel Universal company
1130 Walnut Street, Kansas City, Missouri 64106

www.andrewsmcmeel.com

ISBN: 978-1-4494-3703-9

Library of Congress Control Number: 90-85466

14 15 16 17 SDB 10 9 8 7 6 5 4 3 2

This 2013 edition printed for Barnes & Noble, Inc.

WHO MADE THIS MESS OUT HERE?!

IT WASN'T *ME*, MOM! IT WAS...UH.. IT WAS...

IT WAS A HORRIBLE LITTLE VENUSIAN WHO MATERIALIZED IN THE KITCHEN! HE TOOK OUT SOME DIABOLICAL HIGH-FREQUENCY DEVICE, POINTED IT AT VARIOUS OBJECTS, AND...

MOTHERS ARE THE NECESSITY OF INVENTION.

I'M HO-OME!

WHAT DID YOU DO, STEP ON A LAND MINE?

WHEN'S DAD EVER GOING TO BUILD THAT TIGER PIT I KEEP ASKING HIM ABOUT?

CALVIN, WHERE ARE YOU? GET OUT HERE!

COME ON, CALVIN, I'M GETTING TIRED OF THIS!

I *MEAN* IT, CALVIN! COME OUT AND TAKE YOUR BATH! *NOW!*

SOONER OR LATER SHE'S GOING TO HAVE TO QUESTION WHETHER THIS IS REALLY WORTH THE TROUBLE.

CALVIN AND HOBBES

by WATTERSON

IF *I* WAS IN CHARGE, WE'D NEVER SEE GRASS BETWEEN OCTOBER AND MAY.

ON "THREE", READY? ONE... TWO... THREE!

SNOW!

I SAID SNOW! C'MON! SNOW!

SNOW!

OK THEN, *DON'T* SNOW! SEE WHAT *I* CARE! I *LIKE* THIS WEATHER! LET'S HAVE IT FOREVER!

PLEEAASE SNOW! PLEASE ?? JUST A FOOT! OK, EIGHT INCHES! THAT'S ALL! C'MON! SIX INCHES, EVEN! HOW ABOUT JUST SIX ??

I'M *WAAIIITING...*

RRRRGGHHH

DO YOU WANT ME TO BECOME AN ATHEIST?

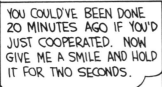

CaLviN and HObbEs

by WATTERSON

AHH... THE PERFECT SLUSHBALL!

HARD ENOUGH TO STING, YET SLOPPY ENOUGH TO DRIBBLE DOWN THE COLLAR AND SOAK THE UNDERGARMENTS.

HERE COMES SUSIE! NOW'S MY CHANCE TO HIT HER WITH A SLUSHBALL!

I SEE YOU! YOU'D BETTER NOT THROW THAT! SANTA CLAUS IS WATCHING YOU RIGHT NOW!

FWISSHHH!

ZINGG

WHAP!

OH YES! YES! IT WAS WORTH IT! WHAT A SHOT! I'M NOT SORRY! OH, IT WAS BEAUTIFUL! I'D DO IT AGAIN IN A MINUTE! HA HA!

WATTERSON

SANTA'S GONNA SKIP THIS BLOCK FOR YEARS.

MOMM! MOM!

WHAT IS IT? WHAT'S THE MATTER?

DO PEOPLE GROW FROM SPORES?

SPORES?!? YOU WAKE ME UP AT 2 AM. TO ASK IF PEOPLE GROW FROM *SPORES?* ARE YOU OUT OF YOUR MIND?? WHY ARE YOU EVEN AWAKE?! GO TO SLEEP!!

SHE DIDN'T ANSWER. SHE MUST NOT KNOW.

I'M TELLING YOU, IT'S TRUE.

I SAY IT'S A FALLACY THAT KIDS NEED 12 YEARS OF SCHOOL! THREE MONTHS IS PLENTY!

LOOK AT ME. I'M SMART! I DON'T NEED 11½ MORE YEARS OF SCHOOL! IT'S A COMPLETE WASTE OF MY TIME!

HOW ON EARTH DID YOU GET ALL THE WAY TO THE BUS STOP WITH BOTH FEET THROUGH ONE PANT LEG?

I FELL DOWN A LOT.

... WHY? WHAT'S YOUR POINT?

NOTHING. I WAS JUST CURIOUS.

HOW'S MY PEANUT BUTTER SANDWICH COMING? YOU'RE USING CHUNKY PEANUT BUTTER, RIGHT? I WON'T EAT SMOOTH!

MAKE IT AN OPEN FACE SANDWICH, TOO! DON'T PUT ANY JELLY ON IT OR ANYTHING! AND USE SOME NORMAL BREAD! I DON'T LIKE THOSE WEIRD GRAIN BREADS!

DID YOU CUT IT DIAGONALLY? I LIKE TRIANGLES BETTER THAN RECTANGLES, SO BE SURE TO CUT IT RIGHT!

YOUR MAJESTY'S SANDWICH.

HEY, THIS IS A CLOSED-FACE, HORIZONTALLY CUT, SMOOTH PEANUT BUTTER SANDWICH ON WEIRD BREAD WITH JELLY! WEREN'T YOU *LISTENING?!*

BOY, DID I GET IN TROUBLE AT SCHOOL TODAY. WOW.

WHAT HAPPENED?

I DON'T EVEN WANT TO TALK ABOUT IT.

DID IT HAVE ANYTHING TO DO WITH ALL THOSE SIRENS ABOUT NOON?

I *SAID* I DON'T WANT TO TALK ABOUT IT.

DID YOU BRING SOMETHING FOR SHOW AND TELL?

YOU BET!

I BROUGHT THESE CHARRED ROCKS AND ASHES FROM MY BACK YARD.

SEE? DRAMATIC PROOF THAT UFOs LANDED NOT A HUNDRED FEET FROM MY HOUSE! THEIR RETRO ROCKETS BURNED SOLID ROCK INTO THIS FRAGILE GRAY DUST CUBE!

THIS IS AN OLD CHARCOAL BRIQUETTE.

EVEN AS WE SPEAK, ALIENS ARE UNDOUBTEDLY INFILTRATING THE HIGHEST LEVELS OF OUR GOVERNMENT.

DISGUSTING DENIZEN OF THE DEEP, THE GIANT OCTOPUS GLIDES ACROSS THE OCEAN FLOOR.

AT THE SIGHT OF AN ENEMY, HE RELEASES A CLOUD OF INK AND MAKES HIS GETAWAY!

MISS WORMWOOD!

CALVIN and HOBBES

by WATTERSON

WELL, IT'S A NEW YEAR.

AND I'D SAY THE FIRST 10 HOURS HAVEN'T BEEN UP TO SNUFF.

DID YOU MAKE ANY NEW YEAR'S RESOLUTIONS?

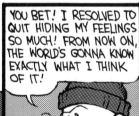

YOU BET! I RESOLVED TO QUIT HIDING MY FEELINGS SO MUCH! FROM NOW ON, THE WORLD'S GONNA KNOW EXACTLY WHAT I THINK OF IT!

YES, YOU'VE CERTAINLY BEEN THE MODEL OF SELF-RESTRAINT AND UNDER-STATEMENT UP UNTIL NOW.

WELL NO MORE.

AND I'VE *ALSO* RESOLVED NOT TO PUT UP WITH SARCASTIC TIGERS.

IF I SEE ANY, I'LL TELL THEM.

18

19

WHAT DO YOU THINK IS THE BEST WAY TO GET WHAT YOU WANT? IS IT BETTER TO HOLD FAST AND NEVER BACK DOWN, OR TO COMPROMISE?

I SUPPOSE IT'S BEST TO HOLD FAST WHEN YOU CAN, AND COMPROMISE WHEN YOU NEED TO.

THAT'S A LOT MORE MATURE THAN I THINK I CARE TO BE.

I THINK THE SHORT ATTENTION SPAN OF TELEVISION IS GREAT.

AS FAR AS *I'M* CONCERNED, IF SOMETHING IS SO COMPLI- CATED THAT YOU CAN'T EXPLAIN IT IN 10 SECONDS, THEN IT'S PROBABLY NOT WORTH KNOWING ANYWAY.

MY TIME IS VALUABLE. I CAN'T GO THINKING ABOUT ONE SUBJECT FOR MINUTES ON END. I'M A BUSY MAN.

...WHO'S BEEN SITTING HERE FOR THREE HOURS.

... AT SIX THOUGHTS A MINUTE.

THERE'S SOMETHING MAGICAL ABOUT HAVING A FIRE.

THE CRACKLES AND SNAPS, THE WARM, FLICKERING LIGHT... EVERYTHING ALWAYS SEEMS SAFE AND COZY IF YOU'RE SITTING IN FRONT OF A FIRE.

AND IF YOU'VE GOT A HOT TIGER TUMMY TO LIE AGAINST.... *WELL!*

Z

THE BAY DOORS OPEN AND OUT FALLS CALVIN, THE C-BOMB!

CALVIN IS ABOUT TO UNLEASH THE PURE DESTRUCTIVE FORCE OF A MILLION A-BOMBS!

THE WORLD GASPS IN HORROR AS HE STREAKS TOWARD HIS TARGET!

OH NO YOU DON'T!!

WILL YOU READ THIS TONIGHT? "AN ODE TO TIGERS"?

HOBBES WROTE IT. "THE ZEBRA'S STRIPES ARE LACKING HUES, SO THEY DON'T COMPARE TO YOU-KNOW-WHOSE."

"ORANGE, BLACK AND WHITE IS WHAT TO WEAR! IT'S HAUTE COUTURE FOR THOSE WHO DARE! IT'S CAMOUFLAGE, AND STYLISH, TOO! YES, TIGERS LOOK THE BEST, IT'S TRUE!"

THIS GOES ON? FOR PAGES. PRETTY TEDIOUS, ISN'T IT?

I'M HO-OME!

KAPOW!

WUMPH!

GREAT. THE SNOW CUSHIONED THE BLOW TO MY SPINE, SO NOW I CAN DIE OF PNEUMONIA. AWW, HAS OO GOT DE SNIFFOOS?

CALVIN and HOBBES

by WATTERSON

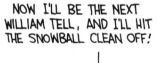

OK, LET'S SEE... IF THE WIND IS BLOWING NORTH-NORTHEAST AT 6 MPH, AND I THROW THE SNOWBALL DUE WEST AT 90 MPH WITH A SLIGHT TOP SPIN....

HA! SUSIE DIDN'T EVEN HEAR ME SNEAK UP!

NOW I'LL CREAM HER CRANIUM WITH A BARRAGE OF SNOWBALLS!

WHIZZZ

PIFF

PIFF

THESE DARN CROSS BREEZES! SHE DIDN'T EVEN NOTICE!

YOU'RE THE WORST SHOT IN THE WORLD, CALVIN! IF IT WASN'T FOR GRAVITY, YOU PROBABLY COULDN'T EVEN HIT THE GROUND!

SMACK!

I DID IT! I DID IT! JUST WHEN IT REALLY COUNTED, I *DID* IT! HA HA HA! RIGHT IN THE KISSER! HA HA!

BAD NEWS, MOM. I PROMISED MY SOUL TO THE DEVIL THIS AFTERNOON.

OH? THAT RECENTLY?

THE FEARLESS SPACEMAN SPIFF FINDS HIMSELF ON THE PLANET CLOSEST TO STAR X-351!

AN ALIEN APPROACHES... BUT IN THE BLINDING LIGHT, OUR HERO CAN HARDLY MAKE IT OUT! IS IT FRIENDLY OR HOSTILE?

WHAT ARE YOU DOING IN BED STILL?! GET READY FOR SCHOOL!

DEFINITELY HOSTILE.

THE SCHOOL BUS WILL BE HERE ANY MINUTE! GO! SCOOT!

SPACEMAN SPIFF, CAPTURED BY VICIOUS ZOGWARGS, IS ABOUT TO BE TRANSPORTED TO THE LABOR CAMP! OUR HERO HATCHES A BOLD PLAN!

AT THE LAST SECOND, SPIFF MAKES HIS BREAK! TAKING ADVANTAGE OF THE PLANET'S WEAKER GRAVITY, OUR HERO IS AWAY LIKE A SHOT.

THERE'S THE BUS... BUT WHY DON'T I SEE CALVIN?

SPIFF ESCAPES!

DID CALVIN GET ON THE BUS?

I DIDN'T SEE. ...WHY?

SOMEONE JUST DARTED BEHIND THAT TREE. SEE, THERE HE GOES AGAIN! ISN'T THAT CALVIN?

THE ZOGWARGS HAVE SPOTTED HIM! OUR HERO INFLATES THE EMERGENCY JET PACK HE KEEPS IN HIS POCKET, AND PREPARES FOR TAKEOFF!

CALVIN, WHAT ARE YOU DOING? YOU'RE SUPPOSED TO BE ON THE SCHOOL BUS! GET OVER HERE!

OUR HERO BLASTS OFF WITH HIS EMERGENCY JET PACK! ANOTHER DARING ESCAPE FOR THE INTREPID SPACEMAN SPIFF!

ZOUNDS! THE ZOGWARGS ARE ON ROCKET SCOOTERS! SPIFF FIRES HIS DEATH RAY BLASTER!

IT'S YOUR OWN GRAVE YOU'RE DIGGING, BUSTER!

YOUNG MAN, YOU ARE IN *VERY* BIG TROUBLE!

WHY DIDN'T YOU GET ON THE SCHOOL BUS?! NOW *I'VE* GOT TO DRIVE YOU, AND YOUR DAD WILL BE LATE FOR WORK!

YOU'VE INCONVENIENCED EVERYONE! WHAT HAVE YOU GOT TO SAY FOR YOURSELF?!

GIVE ME LIBERTY OR GIVE ME DEATH, ZOGWARG QUEEN!

DON'T TEMPT ME! AND LISTEN, YOU CALL ME "MOM," ...GOT IT?

HEY, CALVIN, HOW COME YOU'RE LATE TODAY? WHY DIDN'T YOU RIDE THE BUS?

I WAS GOING TO SKIP SCHOOL, BUT I GOT CAUGHT.

REALLY? HOW?

MOM HAD THE WIND FOR THAT FINAL SPRINT.

YOUR MOM HAD TO *CHASE* YOU?

I COULDN'T BELIEVE IT WHEN SHE CLEARED THE HEDGE.

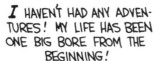
 GET A LOAD OF *THIS* DUMB ASSIGNMENT! I'M SUPPOSED TO WRITE ABOUT AN ADVENTURE I'VE HAD!

 *I* HAVEN'T HAD ANY ADVENTURES! MY LIFE HAS BEEN ONE BIG BORE FROM THE BEGINNING!

 HAVE I EVER BEEN ABDUCTED BY PIRATES? HAVE I EVER FACED DOWN A CHARGING RHINO? HAVE I EVER BEEN IN A SHOOT-OUT, OR ON A BOMBING RAID? **NO!** I NEVER GET TO HAVE ADVENTURES!

 WHAT ABOUT THE TIME YOU BACKED THE CAR THROUGH THE GARAGE DOOR?

YOU CALL THAT AN ADVENTURE? I DIDN'T EVEN GET ON THE HIGHWAY.

 WHEN DO YOU THINK WE'LL GET A THUNDER AND LIGHTNING STORM?

 I DON'T KNOW. PROBABLY NOT UNTIL SPRING.

 I THINK HE'S GOING TO MELT BEFORE WE CAN BRING HIM TO LIFE.

 HEY, SUSIE, STAND ON THIS "X."

WHY?

 NO REASON. JUST DO IT. I DARE YOU.

NO.

 PLEASE? C'MON!

GET LOST.

 THIS MAY NOT WORK OUT AS WELL AS I THOUGHT.

WOW, YOU'VE MADE A LOT OF SNOWMEN TODAY!

YEP. THEY'RE EFFIGIES. EACH ONE REPRESENTS SOMEONE I HATE.

WHEN THE SUN COMES OUT, I'LL WATCH THEIR FEATURES SLOWLY MELT DOWN THEIR DRIPPING BODIES UNTIL THEY'RE NOTHING BUT NOSES AND EYES FLOATING IN POOLS OF WATER.

I WASN'T AWARE YOU EVEN KNEW THIS MANY PEOPLE.

THE ONES I *REALLY* HATE ARE SMALL, SO THEY'LL GO FASTER.

I'M WRITING A BOOK ABOUT MY LIFE.

IT'S CALLED, "CALVIN: THE SHOCKING TRUE STORY OF THE BOY WHOSE EXPLOITS PANICKED A NATION."

INTERESTING TITLE.

THANKS.

SPECIFICALLY WHAT EXPLOITS ARE YOU REFERRING TO?

THAT'S THE PROBLEM. CAN YOU HELP ME THINK OF SOME I COULD DO?

HI, SUSIE.

GO AWAY, CALVIN! SIT SOMEWHERE ELSE! I DON'T WANT TO KNOW WHAT REVOLTING THING YOU HAVE FOR LUNCH TODAY.

RELAX, SUSIE. I'M NOT GOING TO TELL YOU WHAT I HAVE.

YOU'D BETTER NOT. I MEAN IT.

ALL I'LL SAY IS THAT I SURE FEEL SORRY FOR MY TAPEWORM.

MISS WORMWOOD!

HEY! DID I *SAY* WHAT MY LUNCH IS?! *DID* I ?!?

CALVIN and HOBBES

by WATTERSON

WHAT'S THIS?

A CRASH TEST DUMMY. NOW I CAN SEE IF THE HILL IS SAFE TO GO DOWN.

OFF YOU GO!

OOH, I THINK I'M GOING TO BE SICK.

WELL I WOULDN'T HAVE STEERED LIKE *THAT!* HE DESERVED IT!

OH, NO! THE AIR PRESSURE IN THIS ROOM IS TOO HIGH!

CALVIN'S ORGANS ARE IN DANGER OF COLLAPSING! HE...HE'S ABOUT TO IMPLODE!

WE'VE GOT TO GET OUT OF HERE! THERE'S TOO MUCH ATMOSPHERE!

SIT STILL AND BEHAVE. WE CAN'T EAT AT FAST FOOD PLACES ALL THE TIME.

THESE TELEVISION PROGRAMS SURE ARE ROTTEN.

THERE ISN'T AN OUNCE OF IMAGINATION IN THE WHOLE BUNCH. WHAT BILGE.

WHO DO THEY THINK IS STUPID ENOUGH TO SIT AND WATCH THIS TRASH?

YOU.

IF THERE WAS ANYTHING *BETTER* ON, I'D WATCH *THAT.*

YOU'RE TAKING A SHOWER *NOW*? THAT MEANS YOU'RE GOING OUT TONIGHT, RIGHT?

AND YOU HAVEN'T TOLD *ME* TO GET CLEANED UP, SO THAT MEANS I'M STAYING HOME, RIGHT?

AND IF I'M STAYING HOME, THAT MEANS YOU'VE GOTTEN ME A BABY SITTER, RIGHT? AND THAT MEANS YOU'VE PROBABLY HIRED *ROSALYN*, RIGHT?!?

BRILLIANT, HOLMES.

AAAHH HAHH!

QUICK, HOBBES! WE'VE GOT TO HIDE! MOM AND DAD GOT *ROSALYN* FOR OUR BABY SITTER AGAIN! AND YOU KNOW WHAT *THAT* MEANS!

IT USUALLY MEANS WE'RE IN BED BY 6:30.

RIGHT! NO TV, NO HORSING AROUND, *NOTHING*! SHE JUST WALKS IN AND SENDS US STRAIGHT TO BED!

AND THEN SHE DOESN'T EVEN KISS US GOOD NIGHT.

EWW, GROSS! YOU *WANT* HER TO?!?

WHERE ARE YOU GOING TONIGHT? WHY CAN'T HOBBES AND I COME? WHY DO WE HAVE TO HAVE A BABY SITTER?

WE'RE GOING TO DINNER AND A MOVIE JUST TO HAVE SOME TIME TO OURSELVES, OK?

BUT WE COULD COME! HOBBES PROMISES NOT TO KILL ANYONE! WE'D BE GOOD! REALLY! WHY WON'T YOU LET US COME? WHY DON'T YOU WANT US AROUND?

IS THE MOVIE DIRTY? WHAT'S THE PROBLEM?!

GOSH, A DINNER WITH REAL PAUSES IN THE CONVERSATION! CAN YOU IMAGINE?

CALVIN, YOU'VE GOT TWO SECONDS TO UNLOCK THIS DOOR AND GIVE ME BACK MY SCIENCE NOTES!

YOU KNOW, ROSALYN, I'D SUGGEST YOU ADOPT A MORE HUMBLE ATTITUDE. YOU WOULDN'T WANT ANYTHING TO *HAPPEN* TO THESE NOTES, WOULD YOU?

YOU SCUMMY LITTLE TROLL! WHEN YOUR PARENTS GET HOME, I'LL...

FLUSH   AUGH!

THERE'S *ONE* PAGE!

YOU'D BETTER NOT HAVE REALLY FLUSHED ANY OF MY NOTES! I'VE GOT A BIG TEST TOMORROW!

WELL THEN, WITH THAT AT STAKE, OUR DEMANDS SHOULD SEEM VERY REASONABLE!

DEMANDS?! YOU DON'T GET ANY DEMANDS! UNLOCK THIS DOOR!

BOY, YOU'D THINK A HIGH SCHOOL SENIOR WOULD CATCH ON QUICKER. WE SHOULD WRITE THE SCHOOL BOARD.

TORPEDO TUBE READY, CAP'N!

I SURE HOPE YOU MEMORIZED THIS PAGE ALREADY, BECAUSE YOU'RE NEVER GOING TO SEE IT AGAIN!

NO! DON'T FLUSH IT! TELL ME WHAT YOUR STUPID DEMANDS ARE.

THAT'S MORE LIKE IT! OK, FIRST WE WANT TO STAY UP UNTIL MY PARENTS DRIVE IN. SECOND, WE WANT YOU TO GO PICK UP A PIZZA AND RENT US A VIDEO PLAYER...

YOU'RE OUT OF YOUR MIND!

THIRD ... ARE YOU WRITING THESE DOWN?

HERE WE ARE, POISED ON THE PRECIPICE OF "SUICIDE SLOPE." BELOW US LIE THE SKELETAL REMAINS OF HUNDREDS OF LITTLE SLED RIDERS.

SEARCHING FOR THAT ULTIMATE ADRENALINE RUSH, WE PREPARE TO HURL OURSELVES OVER THE BRINK! WHAT FATE AWAITS US?

READY?

NO.

LIFE AND DEATH HANG IN THE BALANCE! A FRACTION OF A SECOND AND ONE WRONG TURN ARE ALL THAT SEPARATE THEM!

THIS ISN'T HELPING.

DAD SAYS THE ANTICIPATION OF HAVING SOMETHING IS OFTEN MORE FUN THAN ACTUALLY HAVING IT.

I THINK HE'S CRAZY. I HATE WAITING FOR THINGS. I LIKE TO HAVE EVERYTHING IMMEDIATELY.

I CAN'T THINK OF *ANY*THING I'D RATHER ANTICIPATE THAN HAVE RIGHT AWAY. CAN YOU?

DEATH COMES TO MIND.

I DON'T KNOW WHY I BOTHER TRYING TO HAVE A LITTLE DISCUSSION WITH YOU WHEN YOU'RE ALWAYS SO MORBID.

I WISH SNOW WAS DRY, SO THAT YOU DIDN'T GET ALL COLD AND WET WHEN YOU PLAYED IN IT.

...THEN AGAIN, IF SNOW WAS DRY, YOU COULDN'T PACK IT INTO SNOWBALLS. THAT WOULDN'T BE GOOD.

I WISH IT SNOWED IN SUMMER. WOULDN'T THAT BE FUN? ...WELL NO, ACTUALLY THAT WOULD MAKE IT HARD TO RUN WHEN YOU PLAY BASEBALL.

HECK, IT'S OK JUST THE WAY IT IS.

WE'RE GLAD YOU APPROVE.

YOU CAN ALWAYS TELL WHEN YOU GET TO *OUR* HOUSE.

I THINK OUR SNOW FORTS ARE TOO FAR APART.

POP!

NOW LET'S SEE IF MOM JUMPS OUT OF *HER* SKIN!

CALVIN and HOBBES by WATTERSON

THE PTERANODON SPREADS HIS GIANT WINGS, AND..

LOOK AT THIS, HOBBES! I COULD ORDER AN OFFICIAL CHOCOLATE FROSTED SUGAR BOMBS BEANIE!

SEE, IT HAS A BATTERY-POWERED PROPELLER ON TOP AND A BIG STAR ON THE FRONT! ISN'T THAT NEAT?

YOU HAVE TO SEND IN FOUR BOX "PROOF OF PURCHASE SEALS" TO GET IT, IT SAYS.

WELL, DON'T JUST STAND THERE, OR THIS'LL TAKE FOREVER.

UGH. THIS STUFF ALWAYS MAKES MY HEART SKIP.

BLECHH. I FEEL SICK.

OH, C'MON, THAT'S ONLY YOUR SECOND BOWL OF CEREAL.

THIS STUFF IS PURE SUGAR.

BUT IT'S *FORTIFIED* WITH EIGHT ESSENTIAL VITAMINS, SO IT'S GOOD FOR YOU.

GIVE ME A BREAK. THIS IS LIKE EATING A BOWL OF MILK DUDS.

LOOK, IT SAYS RIGHT ON THE BOX, "PART OF A WHOLESOME, NUTRITIOUS, BALANCED BREAKFAST."

AND THEY SHOW A GUY EATING FIVE GRAPEFRUITS, A DOZEN BRAN MUFFINS...

YOU KNOW WHY YOU SHAKE LIKE THAT? VITAMIN DEFICIENCY, I'LL BET.

'MORNING, DAD! HOW'S YOUR BREAKFAST?

FINE.

OATMEAL, HUH? A BOWL OF PASTY, BLAND, COLORLESS SLUDGE.

YES. WHY DON'T YOU GO DESCRIBE YOUR *OWN* FOOD SOMEWHERE ELSE?

I'LL BET YOU'D RATHER HAVE A BOWL OF TASTY, LIP-SMACKING, CRUNCHY-ON-THE-OUTSIDE, CHEWY-ON-THE-INSIDE, CHOCOLATE FROSTED SUGAR BOMBS! CAN I POUR YOU SOME?

NO, THANKS. I'M TRYING TO REACH MIDDLE AGE.

WHAT ARE *YOU* HAVING, MOM? BORING OLD TOAST AND TEA?

YOU WANT THE BEANIE, *YOU* EAT THE CEREAL, CALVIN.

 GOSH, I CAN'T WAIT TO GET MY BEANIE! I HOPE IT COMES SOON. DO YOU THINK IT WILL? IT'S PROBABLY BEEN ALMOST SIX WEEKS BY *NOW*, DON'T YOU THINK?

 I ORDERED THE RED BEANIE. BUT WHAT IF IT'S NOT IN STOCK? SHOULD I TAKE THE BLUE ONE, OR WAIT FOR THEM TO REORDER? A BLUE ONE WOULD BE OK, I GUESS, BUT I SURE HOPE THEY HAVE A RED ONE.

 I'VE ALWAYS WANTED A BEANIE LIKE THIS, WITH A PROPELLER. BOY, IT'LL BE SO COOL WHEN I HAVE IT. I CAN'T WAIT. WOW! A RED BEANIE! ... OR A BLUE ONE. DO YOU THINK IT WILL COME TOMORROW? DO YOU?

 IT HAD SURE BETTER.

YEAH, THAT'S HOW I FEEL, TOO.

 THBBPTBTHP

 THBBPTHPPTH

 HOW WAS SCHOOL TODAY?

OH, IT WAS A BLAST! ...DID MY BEANIE COME TODAY?

 PLEASE LET MY BEANIE COME TODAY! I PROMISE I WON'T EVER BE BAD AGAIN! I'LL DO WHATEVER YOU WANT!

 PLEASE, PLEASE, PLEASE! I'LL NEVER ASK ANOTHER FAVOR IF TODAY'S THE DAY I GET MY BEANIE!

 DID I GET MY BEANIE?

NOPE.

 WHAT'S IT TAKE, HUH?!

I CAN'T BELIEVE THIS. EVERY DAY I GET ALL MY HOPES UP, THINKING MY BEANIE WILL COME... AND THEN IT DOESN'T.

AND FOR EACH DAY THAT GOES BY, I FIGURE THE ODDS ARE BETTER THAT IT WILL COME THE *NEXT* DAY, SO MY HOPES GET HIGHER AND HIGHER BEFORE THEY FALL. IT'S AWFUL.

BUT I'VE BEEN DISAPPOINTED SO OFTEN NOW, I'M FINALLY GETTING NUMB TO IT.

MAYBE THE MAILMAN MADE A SECOND TRIP TODAY AND DELIVERED IT IN THE LAST FIVE MINUTES.

WOW! I NEVER THOUGHT OF THAT! C'MON!

HE'S NOT NUMB.

THE LONGER YOU WAIT FOR THE MAIL, THE LESS THERE IS IN IT.

I'M HOME. I DIDN'T GET MY PROPELLER BEANIE TODAY, DID I?

AS A MATTER OF FACT, YOU DID!

IT'S HERE!

HA HA! IT TOOK WEEKS AND WEEKS OF WAITING, BUT AT LONG LAST IT'S HERE! NOW I FINALLY, *FINALLY* GET TO PUT IT ON!

"SOME ASSEMBLY REQUIRED. BATTERIES NOT INCLUDED."

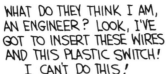

47

Panel 1: DAD, CAN YOU FIX MY BEANIE? I BROKE THE PROPELLER MOTOR TRYING TO PUT IT TOGETHER.

WELL, LET'S SEE.

Panel 2: THIS ISN'T TOO BAD. YOU JUST SNAPPED THE BATTERY CASE. I'LL JUST GLUE IT TOGETHER AND INSERT THE SWITCH FOR YOU, OK?

Panel 3: THERE! GOOD AS NEW! NOW JUST LET THIS SIT AWHILE SO THE GLUE CAN SET.

Panel 4: YOU DID IT! YOU FIXED IT! I CAN'T BELIEVE IT! HEY, MOM! DAD FIXED SOMETHING!

HE DID?? YOUR DAD??

ALL RIGHT! THAT'S ENOUGH!

Panel 5: LOOK, HOBBES! DAD FIXED MY BEANIE!

Panel 6: WELL? HOW'S IT LOOK?

ADJECTIVES FAIL ME.

Panel 7: I'M TURNING IT ON. READY? HERE GOES.

Panel 8: I DON'T SEEM TO BE LIFTING OFF. THIS IS VERY PECULIAR.

THBBTPTHBB

THAT'S THE WORD I WAS LOOKING FOR.

Panel 9: I'M NOT FLYING! THIS BEANIE DOESN'T MAKE ME FLY!

Panel 10: WHAT'S THE POINT OF A PROPELLER BEANIE IF YOU CAN'T EVEN FLY WHEN YOU WEAR IT?!

NOT "STYLE," CERTAINLY.

Panel 11: WHAT A RIP-OFF! I ATE ALL THAT CEREAL, WAITED WEEKS AND WEEKS TO GET THE BEANIE, ASSEMBLED IT MYSELF, AND THE DUMB THING DOESN'T EVEN FLY!

Panel 12: AT LEAST IT'S NOT A TOTAL LOSS. IT CAME IN THIS GREAT CARDBOARD BOX.

OH, BOY! NOW WE'LL HAVE SOME FUN!

CALVIN and HOBBES by WATTERSON

I CAN NEVER ENJOY SUNDAYS, BECAUSE IN THE BACK OF MY MIND I ALWAYS KNOW I'VE GOT TO GO TO SCHOOL THE NEXT DAY.

IT'S LIKE TRYING TO ENJOY YOUR LAST MEAL BEFORE THE EXECUTION.

A PENNY FOR YOUR THOUGHTS

SORRY. *MY* THOUGHTS ARE A BUCK APIECE.

A *DOLLAR*?! THAT'S OUTRAGEOUS! YOUR THOUGHTS AREN'T WORTH THAT!

THIS ONE IS! AT A DOLLAR, IT'S THE BARGAIN OF A LIFETIME.

I WOULDN'T PAY A NICKEL FOR ANY THOUGHT YOU'VE EVER HAD IN YOUR WHOLE FLEA-RIDDEN EXISTENCE!

THAT LITTLE REMARK JUST MADE THE PRICE *TEN* DOLLARS!

TEN?? YOU CAN'T EXTORT ME! *KEEP* YOUR STUPID THOUGHT!

IF YOU KNEW WHAT IT WAS, YOU'D *BEG* TO PAY TEN BUCKS FOR IT.

C'MON, JUST TELL ME WHAT IT IS, WILL YOU?

NOTHING DOING, PAL.

OK, OK! I'LL GIVE YOU 25 CENTS. THAT'S ALL I HAVE.

LET'S SEE IT.

HERE! 25 CENTS! NOW WHAT'S THIS BIG, EXPENSIVE THOUGHT OF YOURS?!

"A FOOL AND HIS MONEY ARE SOON PAR..."

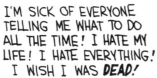

WHAT ARE YOU SO MAD ABOUT ANYWAY? COULDN'T YOU FIND ALL THE BUGS YOU NEEDED FOR YOUR INSECT COLLECTION?

HUH?

HEY, WHERE *IS* YOUR INSECT COLLECTION?? IT'S DUE TODAY.

I FORGOT MY INSECT COLLECTION! OH, NO!!

QUICK! GO HOME AND GET IT! MAYBE YOU CAN MAKE IT BACK BEFORE THE SCHOOL BUS COMES! HURRY! RUN!

NO, THAT'S NOT WHAT I MEANT. HELP ME FIND SOME ANTS.

YOU FORGOT IT *ENTIRELY??*

DON'T JUST STAND THERE, SUSIE! HELP ME CATCH BUGS!

ARE YOU CRAZY?!

WE WERE SUPPOSED TO BE WORKING ON OUR INSECT COLLECTIONS ALL THIS MONTH! YOU CAN'T DO THE WHOLE THING ON THE LAST MORNING WHILE YOU WAIT FOR THE BUS!

HOW COULD YOU HAVE POSSIBLY FORGOTTEN IT, ANYWAY?! IT'S ALL THE CLASS HAS BEEN DOING! WHERE HAVE YOU BEEN?? DON'T YOU PAY ATTENTION?!

DON'T YOU CARE ABOUT GETTING A GOOD EDUCATION?!

IF ANY BUGS FLY IN YOUR OPEN MOUTH, CAN I HAVE THEM?

HERE COMES THE BUS, CALVIN. IT'S HOPELESS.

THERE'S A BUG!

YOU'RE WASTING YOUR TIME! THE TEACHER IS GOING TO KNOW YOU DIDN'T SPEND ANY TIME ON THIS INSECT COLLECTION.

STALL THE BUS DRIVER.

WE'RE SUPPOSED TO HAVE 50 INSECTS! YOU'LL BE LUCKY TO HAVE *ANY!*

GOT IT!

CAN YOU TELL WHAT KIND IT IS? SCRAPE IT OFF.

GET AWAY FROM ME!

PHOOEY. NO BUGS IN THE BUS WINDOW.

I CAN'T BELIEVE YOU'RE DOING THIS.

CHOOL DISTRI

HEY, ASK THAT KID IF HE'S GOT ANY BUGS IN *HIS* WINDOW.

CALVIN, THERE IS NO WAY YOU'RE GOING TO COMPLETE AN INSECT COLLECTION ON THE WAY TO SCHOOL! FORGET IT!

SIGHHH... WELL, MAYBE YOU'RE RIGHT.

HOW MUCH DO YOU WANT FOR *YOUR* COLLECTION? I'LL GIVE YOU A QUARTER...OR HERE, 30 CENTS.

I SPENT A MONTH ON THIS!

HEY, HERE'S A WORM! WORMS ARE BUGS, AREN'T THEY?

EWW GROSS, CALVIN! THAT'S BEEN FLOATING IN A PUDDLE FOR DAYS.

CLASS DOESN'T START FOR 10 MINUTES. IF I CAN CATCH FIVE BUGS A MINUTE, I'LL GET AN "A" ON MY COLLECTION. SEE, I'M OFF TO A GOOD START.

FIVE BUGS A MINUTE?! YOU'RE OUT OF YOUR MIND.

HERE'S ANOTHER ALREADY.

THAT'S A LITTLE BALL OF LINT!

LIKE I'M SURE THE TEACHER'S GOING TO LOOK *REAL CLOSE* AT EVERY HAIRY BUG IN 30 KIDS' COLLECTIONS!

RINNGGGG

THERE'S THE BELL. WE'VE GOT TO GO TO CLASS.

RATS. I DIDN'T GET 50 BUGS YET.

WHAT DO YOU HAVE?

ONE DROWNED WORM, A PIECE OF FUZZY LINT THAT *LOOKS* LIKE A BUG, A LIVE ANT, AND A SMASHED FLY.

WELL, IF YOU LABEL THEM SCIENTIFICALLY IN THE NEXT 30 SECONDS, MAYBE YOU'LL GET AN "F+."

WE'VE GOT TO *LABEL* THESE *TOO*?!? I WAS JUST GOING TO PUT THEM ALL IN AN ENVELOPE.

ACTUALLY, I DON'T THINK THERE'S ANY WAY YOU'LL GET AN "F+."

FOR ALL THIS WORK, I'D BETTER AT LEAST GET A "D."

HERE COMES SUSIE, BACK FROM THE PRINCIPAL'S OFFICE. BOY, DOES SHE LOOK PALE. I WONDER WHAT HAPPENED. SHE'S TALKING TO THE TEACHER NOW.

PSST! SUSIE, WHAT DID THEY DO TO YOU? DID YOU GET EXPELLED? YOU DIDN'T SNITCH ON *ME*, DID YOU?

YOU *DID* SNITCH! YOU'RE A *STOOLIE*! A CANARY!

YOU'RE GOING UP THE RIVER, CALVIN.

CALVIN, WILL YOU COME HERE, PLEASE?

SO *FIRST* I GOT IN TROUBLE FOR NOT PAYING ATTENTION IN CLASS AND FOR TURNING IN A LAST-MINUTE INSECT COLLECTION, WHICH I GOT A "D-MINUS-MINUS" ON.

THEN I GOT IN TROUBLE FOR GETTING *SUSIE* IN TROUBLE WHEN I WANTED HER TO HELP ME FUDGE THE PROJECT.

THEN I GOT IN TROUBLE WHEN I TOLD MOM, AND *THEN* I GOT IN TROUBLE *AGAIN* WHEN *SHE* TOLD *DAD*! I'VE BEEN IN HOT WATER EVER SINCE I GOT UP!

WOW. I'LL BET ALL THIS MAKES YOU GET YOUR BOOK REPORT FINISHED RIGHT ON TIME.

MY WHAT?

ONE OF NATURE'S MOST PECULIAR-LOOKING CREATURES, THE GIRAFFE IS UNIQUELY SUITED TO ITS ENVIRONMENT.

HIS TREMENDOUS HEIGHT ENABLES HIM TO MUNCH ON THE SUCCULENT MORSELS MOST DIFFICULT TO REACH.

CALVIN and HOBBES

by WATTERSON

GOTCHA.!!

HEY! JUST WHAT DO YOU THINK YOU'RE DOING BACK DOWN *HERE?!*

YOU DIDN'T READ ME MY RIGHTS.

DAD! DAD! OUTER SPACE ALIENS JUST LANDED IN THE BACK YARD!

OH, REALLY. WHAT DO THEY LOOK LIKE?

SORT OF LIKE BIG BAKED POTATOES WITH LASER GUNS. I THINK WE SHOULD DO WHAT THEY SAY.

DID THEY SAY WHAT THEY WANT?

YEAH, THEY WANT 10 DOLLARS.

I'LL BET THEY DO.

SINCE YOU'RE SO BUSY, YOU CAN JUST GIVE THE MONEY TO ME, AND I'LL TAKE IT OVER TO THEM.

HOW COME **YOU** ALWAYS READ ME MY BEDTIME STORY AND NOT MOM?

BECAUSE READING THE BEDTIME STORY IS THE **DAD'S** JOB.

AND IT APPEARS TO BE THE **ONLY** "DAD'S JOB" AROUND HERE! LEFT THE DISHES FOR MOM AGAIN, HUH?

TONIGHT'S STORY IS CALLED, "WHY PRINCE CHARMING STAYED SINGLE."

PRINCE **WHAT?**

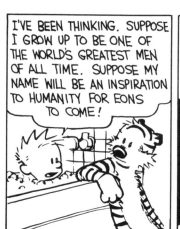

I'VE BEEN THINKING. SUPPOSE I GROW UP TO BE ONE OF THE WORLD'S GREATEST MEN OF ALL TIME. SUPPOSE MY NAME WILL BE AN INSPIRATION TO HUMANITY FOR EONS TO COME!

WHAT WILL THE HISTORY BOOKS SAY? THEY'LL SAY, "MUCH OF HIS CHILDHOOD WAS SPENT UNWILLINGLY IN THE BATHTUB."

WHAT AN INDIGNITY THIS BATH IS! IS THIS SITUATION WORTHY OF ONE OF THE GREATEST MEN OF ALL TIME ?!?

MY LIKELY HISTORICAL SIGNIFICANCE IS A TERRIBLE BURDEN.

WOULD YOU RATHER THEY SAID YOUR CHILDHOOD WAS DIRTY AND SMELLY?

NNNGKGKK

HOCCHHHH

PTOOEY!

BOY, THEY SURE GO FARTHER WHEN YOU MAKE 'EM RIGHT!

LET'S MAKE UP A **NEW** CONTEST, OK?

CALVIN and HOBBES
by WATTERSON

THREE... TWO... ONE...

LIGHT SPEED!

BLASTING ACROSS THE GALAXY IN HYPER LIGHT DRIVE, IT'S *SPACEMAN SPIFF*, INTERPLANETARY EXPLORER EXTRAORDIN...

SINCE CALVIN SEEMS TO BE ENJOYING THE LESSON, LET'S HAVE HIM DEMONSTRATE THE NEXT PROBLEM.

ZOUNDS! A ZOK DEATH SLOOP APPEARS OUT OF NOWHERE AND FRIES SPIFF'S STABILIZERS!

OUR HERO HURLS OUT OF CONTROL TOWARD HIS IMMINENT DOOM!

$$\frac{\begin{array}{r}11\\-3\end{array}}{}$$

THE SITUATION IS DESPERATE! THIS COULD BE THE END! WHAT CAN OUR HERO DO??

HIS MIND RACING FURIOUSLY, SPIFF SPRINGS INTO ACTION! HE DOWNSHIFTS HIS SPACECRAFT AND...

... STALLS.

RINGG!

OH, DARN, OUT OF TIME.

ONCE AGAIN SPACEMAN SPIFF BEATS ALL ODDS TO SAVE THE DAY!

61

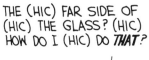

THESE (HIC) HICCUPS ARE DRIVING ME (HIC) CRAZY.

EAT A SPOONFUL OF SUGAR. THAT'S SUPPOSED TO HELP.

I'LL (HIC) TRY ANYTHING.

CRUNCH SMACK SMACK

WELL? ARE YOU CURED?

(HIC) NOPE. I'D BETTER (HIC) EAT SOME MORE.

WATTERSON

MY HICCUPS ARE GONE! THEY FINALLY WENT AWAY ALL BY THEMSELVES! WHAT A RELIEF!

AUGHH!

DID I SCARE YOU? DID I CURE YOUR HICCUPS?

HIC HIC HIC HIC HIC HIC HIC HIC HIC HIC HIC

WATTERSON

LOOK, CALVIN, I BROUGHT HOME SOME JELLY DOUGHNUTS. WOULD YOU LIKE ONE?

NO, JELLY DOUGHNUTS GROSS ME OUT. THEY'RE LIKE EATING GIANT, SQUISHY BUGS. YOU BITE INTO THEM AND ALL THEIR PURPLE GUTS SPILL OUT THE OTHER END.

YOU CAN EAT THEM.

MY FRIENDS ASK ME HOW I STAY THIN.

WATTERSON

CALVIN and HOBBES

by WATTERSON

I'M HOME!

YAHHH!

SLAM!

WHAT A CHUMP!

KNOCK KNOCK

FORGET IT, YOU MORON! I'M NOT OPENING THE DOOR! YOU CAN JUST STAY OUT THERE ALL NIGHT!

OH, I CAN'T *WAIT* TO HEAR *THIS* ONE EXPLAINED.

COME ON, CALVIN! WE WERE SUPPOSED TO HAVE LEFT A HALF-HOUR AGO.

WHERE ARE WE GOING?

FOR THE HUNDREDTH TIME, WE'RE GOING TO A WEDDING. NOW GET IN THE CAR. YOUR DAD'S WAITING.

BUT WHAT IF I FORGOT SOMETHING?

WE'RE ONLY GOING TO BE GONE OVERNIGHT. YOU'LL GET BY.

TURN AROUND! WE FORGOT HOBBES! STOP THE CAR!

WE CAN'T TURN AROUND, CALVIN. WE'RE LATE ALREADY.

BUT DA-AD!!

YOU COULD'VE BEEN READY ON TIME AND HAD ALL YOUR THINGS TOGETHER, BUT YOU PUT UP A FUSS ABOUT GOING, MADE US LATE, AND YOU FORGOT YOUR TIGER. IT'S YOUR OWN FAULT.

YOU'D TURN AROUND IF WE'D FORGOTTEN MOM!

THAT'S BECAUSE SHE'S THE ONLY ONE WHO KNOWS WHERE THIS PLACE IS.

HAR HAR.

WHEN IS THIS DUMB WEDDING GOING TO BE OVER?! I DON'T EVEN KNOW THESE PEOPLE.

THIS WOULD BE A LOT MORE FUN IF HOBBES WAS HERE. I CAN'T BELIEVE WE LEFT HIM AT HOME.

I HOPE HE'S OK. WHAT'S HE GOING TO EAT? WE DIDN'T LEAVE ANY FOOD OUT, AND WE'LL BE GONE ALMOST TWO WHOLE DAYS! HOBBES WILL BE STARVING!

I THINK I'LL LET DAD GO INTO THE HOUSE FIRST.

HOBBES? ARE YOU DOWN HERE? YOU'VE GOT TO BE *SOME*WHERE!

HERE HE IS, CALVIN! I FOUND HOBBES!

YOU *FOUND* HIM! IS HE OK?? HE'S NOT HURT, IS HE?

HE'S FINE. HE WAS UNDER THE BED COVERS.

HOBBES, I'M SO GLAD TO SEE YOU!! YOU'RE SAFE AND SOUND! (SNIFF) AND NOW I AM, TOO!

IT LOOKS LIKE WE'RE A WHOLE FAMILY AGAIN.

SUCH AS IT IS, YES.

...AND THE TELEVISION'S GONE, TOO.

DO YOU HAPPEN TO HAVE THE SERIAL NUMBER?

I'LL BET THE BURGLARS GOT SCARED OFF WHEN THEY SAW THERE WAS A TIGER IN THE HOUSE! HOBBES WAS HERE THE WHOLE TIME!

CALVIN, NOT NOW, OK? I'M BUSY.

NOBODY STICKS AROUND LONG WHEN HE SEES A TIGER, THAT'S FOR SURE! MANDIBLES OF DEATH, THAT'S WHAT HOBBES HAS!

RIGHT. WHY DON'T YOU GO TELL YOUR MOM?

MAYBE HOBBES SHOULD LOOK AT SOME MUG SHOTS. CAN WE GO TO THE STATION AND IDENTIFY SUSPECTS? HUH, CAN WE?

DEAR!

I SURE MEET THE WEIRDOS IN THIS JOB...

I'VE SWEPT UP MOST OF THE GLASS FROM THE WINDOW.

OK, I'LL GET SOMETHING TO COVER UP THE HOLE.

DO YOU THINK IT'S SAFE TO STAY HERE TONIGHT? SUPPOSE THE BURGLARS COME BACK!

THE POLICE SAID THEY'D DRIVE BY, AND WE'LL LEAVE LOTS OF LIGHTS ON.

UGH, IT'S SO CREEPY KNOWING THESE GOONS HAVE BEEN IN OUR HOUSE. I DON'T FEEL SAFE AT ALL.

I KNOW. AND THIS MUST *REALLY* BE SCARY FOR A LITTLE KID LIKE CALVIN.

GOSH, I CAN'T WAIT TO TELL EVERYONE AT SCHOOL HOW OUR HOUSE GOT ROBBED!

BE SURE TO SAY WHO SCARED THE BURGLARS AWAY AFTER THEY TOOK THE TV AND JEWELRY.

Panel 1:
IS CALVIN ASLEEP?

YES, HE'S SNUGGLED UP WITH HOBBES.

Panel 2:
BOY, I DON'T KNOW HOW *I'M* EVER GOING TO SLEEP.

ME NEITHER. I CAN'T GET OVER WHAT'S HAPPENED.

Panel 3:
THE IDEA OF SOME CRAZY STRANGER GOING THROUGH OUR HOUSE... *BRRRR!!* I WISH *I* HAD A BIG STUFFED ANIMAL TO FEEL SAFE WITH.

Panel 4:
I GUESS YOU'LL HAVE TO DO.

SO WHAT DO *I* GET TO SNUGGLE? HOW COME *I'M* THE GROWN-UP??

Panel 5:
THIS IS GOING TO BE A LONG NIGHT.

Panel 6:
MY HEART JUMPS AT THE SLIGHTEST SOUND. IT'S ALMOST 2, AND I'M WIDE AWAKE.

Panel 7:
WHEN SOMEONE BREAKS INTO YOUR HOME, IT SHATTERS YOUR LAST ILLUSION OF SECURITY. IF YOU'RE NOT SAFE IN YOUR OWN HOME, YOU'RE NOT SAFE ANYWHERE.

Panel 8:
A MAN'S HOME IS HIS CASTLE, BUT IT SHOULDN'T HAVE TO BE A FORTRESS.

Panel 9:
ARE YOU STILL AWAKE TOO?

MM-HMM. I WAS THINKING.

Panel 10:
IT'S FUNNY... WHEN I WAS A KID, I THOUGHT GROWN-UPS NEVER WORRIED ABOUT ANYTHING. I TRUSTED MY PARENTS TO TAKE CARE OF EVERYTHING, AND IT NEVER OCCURRED TO ME THAT THEY MIGHT NOT KNOW HOW.

Panel 11:
I FIGURED THAT ONCE YOU GREW UP, YOU AUTOMATICALLY KNEW WHAT TO DO IN ANY GIVEN SCENARIO.

Panel 12:
I DON'T THINK I'D HAVE BEEN IN SUCH A HURRY TO REACH ADULTHOOD IF I'D KNOWN THE WHOLE THING WAS GOING TO BE AD-LIBBED.

WELL, AT LEAST WE WEREN'T HOME WHEN OUR HOUSE WAS BROKEN INTO. NO ONE WAS HURT. WE'RE ALL TOGETHER AND OK.

WE LOST A FEW OF OUR NICE THINGS, BUT THINGS DON'T MATTER MUCH REALLY.

IT'S HARD TO BELIEVE HOW OFTEN WE FORGET THAT.

CAN I BE EXCUSED NOW?

YOU DIDN'T FINISH YOUR DINNER.

WELL, I DIDN'T LIKE IT VERY MUCH, AND THERE'S THIS TV SHOW I WANT TO WATCH, SO...

OUR TV WAS STOLEN, REMEMBER?

GOSH, I GUESS I'LL EAT MY ASPARAGUS, DO MY HOMEWORK, AND GO STRAIGHT TO BED, THEN.

AND WE'RE SO PROUD OF HOW YOU HANDLE ADVERSITY.

THIS IS WHERE OUR TELEVISION USED TO BE.

BUT WE DON'T HAVE A TV ANYMORE. NOW WE HAVE A BLANK WALL TO WATCH.

SO HERE I AM, NOT BEING ENTERTAINED.

A POINTLESS EXISTENCE, HUH?

I MEAN, THE WALL IS EVEN PLAIN OLD *WHITE!*

CaLViN and HOBBES

by WATTERSON

I CAN'T SLEEP.

I THINK NIGHTTIME IS DARK SO YOU CAN IMAGINE YOUR FEARS WITH LESS DISTRACTION.

AT NIGHTTIME, THE WORLD ALWAYS SEEMS SO BIG AND SCARY, AND I ALWAYS SEEM SO SMALL.

I WISH I COULD FALL ASLEEP, SO IT WOULD BE MORNING.

SIGHHHHH..

LOOK AT HOBBES. *HE'S* ASLEEP.

HEH HEH...HE SURE LOOKS FUNNY WHEN HE SLEEPS. TIGERS CLOSE THEIR EYES SO TIGHT. I WONDER WHAT HE'S DREAMING ABOUT.

GOOD OL' HOBBES. WHAT A FRIEND.

THINGS ARE NEVER QUITE AS SCARY WHEN YOU'VE GOT A BEST FRIEND.

GOOD NEWS, HOBBES! I'M STARTING A SECRET CLUB, AND YOU CAN BE IN IT!

OH, BOY!

IT'LL BE GREAT! WE'LL THINK OF SECRET NAMES FOR OURSELVES, SECRET CODES FOR OUR SECRET CORRESPONDENCE, A SECRET HANDSHAKE,...

WE'LL HAVE A SECRET CLUB-HOUSE WITH A SECRET KNOCK TO GET IN, AND WE'LL DO BIG, SECRETIVE THINGS!

WHY ALL THE SECRECY?

PEOPLE PAY MORE ATTENTION TO YOU WHEN THEY THINK YOU'RE UP TO SOMETHING.

OK, THE FIRST THING WE NEED IS A NAME FOR OUR SECRET CLUB.

LET'S CALL IT "THE HOBBES FAN CLUB"!

THE HOBBES FAN CLUB?! GIVE ME A BREAK! I'M SURE!!

THIS IS A TOP-SECRET SOCIETY! THE NAME SHOULD BE SOMETHING *MYSTERIOUS*! SOMETHING VAGUELY OMINOUS AND CHILLING!

SOMETHING LIKE, "THE SINISTER ICY BLACK HAND OF DEATH CLUB"?

I STILL LIKE MY IDEA BETTER.

I'VE GOT IT! WE'LL CALL OUR CLUB G.R.O.S.S. — *GET RID OF SLIMY GIRLS!* THAT WAY, SUSIE DERKINS CAN'T JOIN!

IS SHE SLIMY?

ALL GIRLS ARE SLIMY. NOW THE FIRST ORDER OF BUSINESS IS TO ELECT OFFICERS.

I GET TO BE PRESIDENT! I GET TO BE PRESIDENT!

OH, NO YOU DON'T! THIS WHOLE CLUB WAS *MY* IDEA, SO *I* GET TO BE PRESIDENT.

OK, THEN I GET TO BE KING AND TYRANT.

HEY, NO! *THAT'S* WHAT *I* WANT TO BE! YOU CAN BE PRESIDENT!

HI, CALVIN! WHAT ARE YOU DOING, MAKING PAPER HATS? CAN I MAKE ONE, TOO?

DON'T BE RIDICULOUS. THIS IS THE OFFICIAL CHAPEAU OF OUR TOP-SECRET CLUB, G.R.O.S.S. — *GET RID OF SLIMY GIRLS!*

"SLIMY GIRLS"?!

I KNOW THAT'S REDUNDANT, BUT OTHERWISE IT DOESN'T SPELL ANYTHING. NOW GO AWAY.

GIRLS AREN'T SLIMY!

DON'T GET GUNK ON ME. I TOOK A BATH LAST SATURDAY AND I'M ALL CLEAN.

I CAN'T BELIEVE YOU STARTED A SECRET CLUB JUST TO EXCLUDE GIRLS! THERE'S NOTHING WRONG WITH GIRLS!

SEE, HOBBES? GIRLS ARE SO EMOTIONAL.

YOU'RE THE MEANEST, MOST ROTTEN LITTLE KID I KNOW! WELL, FINE! PLAY WITH YOUR STUFFED TIGER! SEE WHAT I CARE! I DON'T WANT TO PLAY WITH A STINKER LIKE YOU ANYWAY!!

WOW, WHAT A GREAT CLUB!

OK, WE'VE GOT A SIGN FOR OUR SECRET CLUB, SO NOW WE NEED TO FIND A SECRET MEETING PLACE.

I KNOW! WE CAN SET UP A CARD TABLE IN THE GARAGE! THAT WOULD BE PERFECT FOR DRAWING UP MAPS AND STUFF!

HMM, THERE'S NOT MUCH ROOM WITH THE CAR HERE. LET'S PUSH IT INTO THE DRIVE.

SHOULDN'T YOU ASK YOUR MOM TO MOVE IT INSTEAD?

NAHH. SHE WON'T CARE IF WE PUSH IT OUT. C'MON.

IN THE PAST, YOU'VE BEEN A REMARKABLY POOR JUDGE OF WHAT YOUR MOM CARES ABOUT.

WHAT'S GOING ON, I WONDER. WHY ARE ALL THOSE CARS SLOWING DOWN AS THEY GO BY?

GOSH, DID SOMEONE HAVE AN ACCIDENT? IT LOOKS LIKE THERE'S A CAR IN THE DITCH! ...BUT I DON'T SEE ANYONE BY IT.

AND HOW ON EARTH DID THEY GO IN STRAIGHT BACKWARD? TO DO THAT, THE CAR WOULD'VE HAD TO COME...

...RIGHT...OUT...OUR... DRIVEWAY!

WELL, MOM'S SURE TO HAVE FOUND THE CAR BY NOW AND GUESSED WHAT WE DID.

NOW I KNOW WHAT THEY MEAN WHEN THEY SAY YOU CAN'T GO HOME AGAIN.

WHAT'S THAT SOUND?

I DON'T HEAR ANYTHING.

THERE! SOMETHING IS CRASHING THROUGH THE BRUSH!

IT SOUNDS BIG! MAYBE IT'S A BEAR!

THERE ARE *BEARS* OUT HERE??

CLIMB THE TREE! CLIMB THE TREE!

IF YOU ASK *ME*, TIGERS ARE THE ONLY FEROCIOUS ANIMALS THE WORLD REALLY NEEDS.

"BOY, 6, KILLED BY BEAR! PARENTS SAVED THE TROUBLE."

CalvIN and HObbEs
by WATTERSON

TRUE FRIENDS ARE HARD TO COME BY.

I NEED MORE MONEY.

I WISH PEOPLE WERE MORE LIKE ANIMALS.

ANIMALS DON'T TRY TO CHANGE YOU OR MAKE YOU FIT IN. THEY JUST ENJOY THE PLEASURE OF YOUR COMPANY.

ANIMALS AREN'T CONDITIONAL ABOUT FRIENDSHIPS. ANIMALS LIKE YOU JUST THE WAY YOU ARE.

THEY LISTEN TO YOUR PROBLEMS, THEY COMFORT YOU WHEN YOU'RE SAD, AND ALL THEY ASK IN RETURN IS A LITTLE KINDNESS.

WHOOONK! *SOB* IT'S SO...SO *TRUE!* HOOOOT! THBPBTPTH.

...AND SPEAKING OF "A LITTLE KINDNESS," I'D HAVE A TUNA FISH SANDWICH ANY TIME SOON THAT YOU HAPPEN TO MAKE ONE...

OF COURSE, *SOME* ANIMALS GET ON YOUR NERVES ONCE IN A WHILE.

WATTERSON

Calvin and Hobbes

by WATTERSON

MILD-MANNERED CALVIN IS STUCK INSIDE DOING MATH PROBLEMS ON A BEAUTIFUL SUNDAY.

NO ONE IS WATCHING! HE DASHES INTO HIS CLOSET! *THIS* IS A JOB FOR...

DEFENDER OF FREEDOM! ADVOCATE OF LIBERTY!

A BRIGHT CRIMSON STREAK BLASTS UP THROUGH THE ATMOSPHERE, AND THEN TURNS BACK TOWARD EARTH!

GAINING STUPENDOUS MOMENTUM, *STUPENDOUS MAN* STRIKES THE GROUND AT AN ACUTE ANGLE WITH STUPENDOUS FORCE!

THE EARTH SLOWLY STOPS ROTATING... AND BEGINS TO TURN IN THE OPPOSITE DIRECTION!

PUSHING WITH ALL HIS MIGHT, *STUPENDOUS MAN* TURNS THE PLANET ALL THE WAY AROUND BACKWARD! THE SUN SETS IN THE EAST AND RISES IN THE WEST! SOON IT'S 10 A.M. THE PREVIOUS DAY!

WHAT ARE YOU DOING OUTSIDE? DID YOU FINISH YOUR HOMEWORK ALREADY?

IT'S SATURDAY! I DON'T NEED TO DO IT UNTIL TOMORROW... THANKS TO *STUPENDOUS MAN!*

HERE'S THE LATEST POLL OF HOUSEHOLD 6-YEAR-OLDS, DAD.

AN OVERWHELMING MAJORITY EXPRESS AMAZEMENT AT HOW LITTLE YOU'VE ACCOMPLISHED AS DAD SO FAR. THE IMPRESSION IS THAT YOU'RE AVOIDING ALL THE HARD DECISIONS THAT NEED TO BE MADE.

IN FACT, NONE OF THOSE POLLED COULD NAME A SINGLE INSTANCE OF TRUE PATERNAL LEADERSHIP.

HOW ABOUT IF I LEAD YOU UPSTAIRS TO YOUR BED?

HA HA. IF WE CAN BE SERIOUS FOR A MOMENT, I HAVE SOME INNOVATIVE IDEAS ABOUT MY ALLOWANCE.

LOOK AT ALL THESE ANTS.

THEY'RE ALL RUNNING LIKE MAD, WORKING TIRELESSLY ALL DAY, NEVER STOPPING, NEVER RESTING.

AND FOR WHAT? TO BUILD A TINY LITTLE HILL OF SAND THAT COULD BE WIPED OUT AT ANY MOMENT! ALL THEIR WORK COULD BE FOR NOTHING, AND YET THEY KEEP ON BUILDING. THEY NEVER GIVE UP!

I SUPPOSE THERE'S A LESSON IN THAT.

YEAH ... ANTS ARE MORONS. LET'S SEE WHAT'S ON TV.

BOY, WHAT A GROUCH.

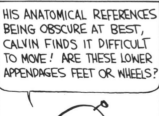

WHERE ARE *YOU* GOING?

OUT.

DID YOU PICK UP YOUR ROOM LIKE I ASKED YOU TO?

NO.

SO WHEN YOU SAY YOU'RE GOING "OUT," YOU REALLY MEAN YOU'RE GOING BACK UPSTAIRS TO CLEAN YOUR ROOM, RIGHT?

ENGLISH MUST NOT BE HER FIRST LANGUAGE.

WHAT ARE YOU DOING DOWN HERE AGAIN? DIDN'T I JUST SEND YOU TO CLEAN YOUR ROOM?!

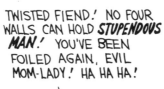

TWISTED FIEND! NO FOUR WALLS CAN HOLD *STUPENDOUS MAN!* YOU'VE BEEN FOILED AGAIN, EVIL MOM-LADY! HA HA HA!

OH YEAH?

GREAT ZOK! SHE'S FIXED HER MIND-SCRAMBLING EYEBALL RAY ON ME! I'M SUDDENLY FILLED WITH THE DESIRE TO GO BACK UPSTAIRS AND DO HER NEFARIOUS BIDDING!

GLAD TO HEAR IT.

"CLEAN UP YOUR ROOM! CLEAN UP YOUR ROOM!" THAT'S ALL I EVER HEAR!

IT'S *MY* ROOM, RIGHT?!? IF *I* DON'T MIND THE MESS, WHAT BUSINESS IS IT OF ANYONE ELSE?! THIS IS TYRANNY! I *HATE* CLEANING MY ROOM!

IT'S GOING TO TAKE ME ALL *DAY* TO DO THIS! OOH, THIS MAKES ME MAD! A WHOLE DAY SHOT! WASTED! DOWN THE DRAIN! GONE!

AARGH!

ARE YOU KIDDING? HOW COULD THIS POSSIBLY TAKE ALL DAY?

HECK, IT'LL BE ANOTHER HOUR BEFORE I'M EVEN THROUGH GRIPING.

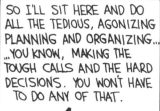

HELP! A BEE! A BEE! RUN FOR YOUR LIFE!

HOBBES! DID YOU SEE IT?? IT WAS THE BIGGEST BEE IN THE WORLD! IT WAS THE SIZE OF A KAISER ROLL! IT MUST'VE WEIGHED 70 POUNDS!

IT SOUNDED LIKE A HELICOPTER, AND ITS STINGER WAS LIKE A HARPOON! IT MUST'VE BEEN A KILLER DEATH BEE! MAN, I'M LUCKY IT DIDN'T GET ME!

LIFE IN THE GREAT SUBURBAN OUTBACK IS CERTAINLY FRAUGHT WITH PERIL.

IF YOU'D SEEN IT, YOU'D HAVE BEEN SCARED, TOO.

I CAN'T IMAGINE MASTERING THE SKILLS INVOLVED HERE WITHOUT A CLEARER UNDERSTANDING OF WHO'S GOING TO BE IMPRESSED.

I SAW THE MAN IN THE MOON TONIGHT.

MM.

I DIDN'T KNOW THE MOON MADE FACES.

THAT'S "PHASES".

Calvin and Hobbes

by Watterson

AHHHH...

UH-OH. SOMETHING IS SERIOUSLY WRONG HERE.

THE LAWS OF PERSPECTIVE HAVE BEEN REPEALED!

OBJECTS NO LONGER DIMINISH IN SIZE WITH DISTANCE!

LINES DO NOT CONVERGE TOWARD ANY POINT ON THE HORIZON!

ALL SPATIAL RELATIONSHIPS ARE LOST! IT'S IMPOSSIBLE TO JUDGE WHERE ANYTHING IS! OH NO!

CALVIN, QUIT RUNNING AROUND AND CRASHING INTO THINGS, OR I'LL SELL YOU TO THE MONKEY HOUSE!

...AND NOW *SHE'S* LOST PERSPECTIVE.

THE GIANT PTERANODON HOPS TO THE EDGE OF THE CLIFF.

THERE HE SPREADS HIS BAT-LIKE WINGS AND TAKES TO THE AIR! SOARING HIGH OVER THE PREHISTORIC VALLEY, THE PTERANODON IS TRULY A MAJESTIC SIGHT!

THAT'S IT, THINK MAJESTIC!

I'M THINKING WE SHOULD'VE PICKED A SMALLER CLIFF!

IT'S TOO DARN HOT OUT HERE.

YOU COULD GO WADING IN THE CREEK.

THIS WATER IS TOO DARN COLD.

YOU COULD GO SIT IN THE SHADE THEN.

THIS SHADE IS TOO DARN DARK.

YOU COULD GO SIT IN YOUR ROOM WITH THE WINDOWS SHUT AND THE FAN AND LIGHTS ON.

THAT'S WHAT I WAS DOING WHEN MOM THREW ME OUT HERE.

I WAS KIDDING.

GIVE ME SOME COOKIES, OR I SOAK YOU WITH THIS WATER BALLOON!

WHY, YOU LITTLE THUG! DON'T YOU THREATEN YOUR MOTHER! AND DON'T EVEN *THINK* ABOUT THROWING THAT IN THE HOUSE!

OUT! OUT!

I'LL BET I'D HAVE GOTTEN SOME COOKIES IF I HAD FILLED THIS WITH *PAINT*.

93

IT'S JULY ALREADY! OH NO! OH NO!

WHAT HAPPENED TO JUNE?! SUMMER VACATION IS SLIPPING THROUGH OUR FINGERS LIKE GRAINS OF SAND!

IT'S GOING TOO FAST! WE'VE GOT TO HOARD OUR FREEDOM AND HAVE MORE FUN! TIME RUSHES ON! HELP! HELP!

I DON'T THINK I WANT TO BE HERE AT THE END OF AUGUST.

AAUGH! IT'S A HALF-HOUR LATER THAN IT WAS HALF AN HOUR AGO! RUN! RUN!

MOM TOOK ME TO THE LIBRARY TODAY, DAD.

THAT'S NICE. DID YOU GET OUT A BOOK?

YEP. IT'S GREAT! I HAD NO IDEA BOOKS COULD BE SO MUCH FUN.

AND YOU'LL LEARN THINGS, TOO.

I'LL SAY! MY BOOK SAYS THAT THIS ONE WASP LAYS ITS EGG ON A SPIDER, SO WHEN THE EGG HATCHES, THE LARVA EATS THE SPIDER, SAVING THE VITAL ORGANS FOR LAST, SO THE SPIDER STAYS ALIVE WHILE IT'S BEING DEVOURED!

GROSS, HUH?

ISN'T THERE A STREET CORNER WHERE HE COULD HANG OUT INSTEAD?

AND COLOR PICTURES, TOO! WANT TO SEE 'EM?

I'M DESTINED FOR GREATNESS, I JUST KNOW IT. "CALVIN THE GREAT," THEY'LL CALL ME.

AND THINK HOW LUCKY *YOU'LL* BE! YOU'LL GET TO TELL EVERYONE HOW YOU KNEW ME AS A KID! WHAT A PRIVILEGE!

IN FACT, ALL THE PAPERS AND MAGAZINES WILL PROBABLY WANT TO INTERVIEW YOU TO FIND OUT WHAT I'M REALLY LIKE.

AND BOY, WILL YOU HAVE TO COUGH UP TO KEEP ME QUIET.

AND WHAT'S *THAT* SUPPOSED TO MEAN?!

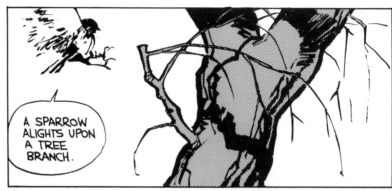

CALViN AND HOBBES

by WATTERSON

CLICK

UH OH...

THE SKY IS A DEEP ORANGE! CALVIN'S SKIN IS A PALE GREEN! YELLOW FLOWERS ARE NOW BLUE!

EVERY COLOR IS THE OPPOSITE OF WHAT IT SHOULD BE!

CALVIN HAS BEEN TRANSFERRED TO A COLOR FILM NEGATIVE!

HIS ONLY HOPE IS TO BE PROCESSED BY A 1-HOUR PHOTO FINISHER! DEVELOPER! I NEED DEVELOPER!

DOGGONE IT, CALVIN! THAT'S ANOTHER PICTURE RUINED! CAN'T YOU LOOK PLEASANT FOR 1/500TH OF A SECOND?!

WHAT ARE YOU WRITING?

I'M TELLING THESE COMPANIES I INTEND TO BOYCOTT ALL THEIR PRODUCTS IF THEY DON'T PULL THEIR ADS FROM A TV SHOW I FIND OFFENSIVE.

BY GOLLY, IF THESE COMPANIES ARE GOING TO SUPPORT OBJECTIONABLE TV PROGRAMS, I'LL TAKE MY BUSINESS ELSEWHERE!

MAYBE I CAN SCARE AWAY THE ADVERTISING DOLLARS AND GET THE SHOW CANCELED.

WHY DON'T YOU JUST NOT WATCH THE SHOW?

THIS CLEAN, WHOLESOME TELEVISION! UGHH, IT MAKES ME SICK.

I NEVER LIKED ICE CREAM CONES TOO MUCH UNTIL I DISCOVERED A NEW WAY TO EAT THEM.

I BITE OFF THE BOTTOM OF THE CONE AND SUCK OUT THE ICE CREAM AS IT GETS SOFT.

YOU WOULDN'T BELIEVE SOME OF THE AWFUL NOISES YOU CAN MAKE, AND IT GETS PRETTY SLOPPY WHEN THE CONE GETS SOGGY AND BOTH ENDS START DRIPPING.

IN MY BOOK, FOOD SHOULD BE NUTRITION AND ENTERTAINMENT.

THAT'S WHY WE TIGERS LIKE OUR FOOD SURPRISED AND RUNNING.

I'M SO SMART IT'S ALMOST SCARY. I GUESS I'M A CHILD PROGENY.

MOST CHILDREN ARE.

HUH?

NOTHING.

PEOPLE THINK IT MUST BE FUN TO BE A SUPER GENIUS, BUT THEY DON'T REALIZE HOW HARD IT IS TO PUT UP WITH ALL THE IDIOTS IN THE WORLD.

ISN'T YOUR PANTS ZIPPER SUPPOSED TO BE IN THE FRONT?

WELL, THERE'S NO DELAYING THE INEVITABLE. LET'S GET IN THE CAR.

WHERE ARE WE GOING?

THE SAME PLACE WE GO *EVERY* SUMMER: CAMPING ON SOME DESOLATE ROCK AT THE END OF THE EARTH.

AGAIN?

YEP. THIS IS HOW DAD LIKES TO UNWIND.

WITH EVERYONE COMPLAINING?

RIGHT. HE LIKES TO WATCH US ALL SUFFER.

LOOK, DAD, THERE'S A TOWN COMING UP. SEE THE SIGN?

WHY DON'T WE PULL OFF, FIND A NICE MOTEL AND JUST STAY *THERE* FOR OUR VACATION? WE COULD SWIM IN THE POOL AND HAVE AIR CONDITIONING AND COLOR CABLE TV AND ROOM SERVICE!

NO ONE WOULD HAVE TO KNOW WE DIDN'T CAMP! *I* WOULDN'T TELL ANYONE! WE COULD EVEN GO TO THE STORE, BUY A BIG FISH, TAKE YOUR PICTURE WITH IT, AND SAY YOU CAUGHT IT! CAN'T WE, DAD? CAN'T WE TURN OFF HERE?

YES, LET'S!

NOW DON'T *YOU* START!

TA DA! WE'RE HERE!

GOOD OL' "ITCHY ISLAND," HOME OF THE NUCLEAR MOSQUITOES.

BUG BITES BUILD CHARACTER.

YEAH, AND LAST YEAR YOU SAID DIARRHEA BUILDS CHARACTER.

SO THINK WHAT A FINE YOUNG MAN YOU'RE GROWING UP TO BE.

...IF ALL THIS CHARACTER DOESN'T KILL ME FIRST.

THAT REMINDS ME, OPEN THE DUFFEL BAG AND GET OUT THE SPAM.

IF THE CANOE ISN'T HERE IN THE MORNING, IT MEANS HOBBES AND I STRUCK OUT FOR HOME.

BOY, IT'S GREAT TO BE HERE! THIS IS THE LIFE! I THINK I'LL JUMP IN FOR A SWIM. WANT TO JOIN ME?

NO, THANKS.

AW, C'MON. IT'LL FEEL GREAT.

RIGHT. THAT LAKE COULDN'T HAVE MELTED BEFORE YESTERDAY.

HEY, LET'S GO FOR A SWIM!

SURE, DAD. I'D LOVE TO START THE WEEK WITH A LITTLE HYPOTHERMIA.

I THINK WHAT I LIKE BEST ABOUT VACATIONS IS THE FAMILY TOGETHERNESS.

WAKE UP, CALVIN. IT'S 5:30 AND YOU CAN SEE THE FISH JUMPING.

MMF. GOWAY.

IT'S A BEAUTIFUL MORNING. THE SUN'S BARELY UP AND THERE'S A MIST OVER THE WATER. IT'S PERFECTLY STILL. NOT A SOUL ANYWHERE! DON'T YOU WANT TO SEE THIS?

LEEMEE LONE.

I THOUGHT YOU SAID YOU WANTED TO GO FISHING. YOU'VE GOT TO GET UP EARLY IF YOU WANT TO CATCH ANY-THING. C'MON, THE CANOE'S ALL READY AND I'VE GOT YOUR FISHING ROD.

MOM, MAKE DAD GO AWAY!

ANOTHER THING I LIKE ABOUT VACATIONS IS THE SHARING OF SPECIAL MOMENTS.

WELL, I GUESS THAT'S ENOUGH FISHING FOR NOW. MMM, I CAN'T WAIT TO GET BACK AND HAVE BREAKFAST! I CAN ALMOST SMELL THE COFFEE FROM HERE! WHAT A LIFE!

HEY, WHERE *IS* EVERY...

THERE'S GOING TO BE A SMALLMOUTH BASS FLOPPING IN SOME SLEEPING BAGS IN A MINUTE OR TWO!

YOU KNOW, I REALLY LIKE IT WHEN YOU GO OFF TO WORK IN THE MORNINGS.

IT'S 6:30 ALREADY! ARE YOU PEOPLE GOING TO WASTE THE WHOLE DAY?

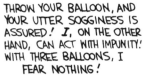

ARR! WE'RE BLOODTHIRSTY PIRATES!

AVAST, YE SCURVY DOGS! HOIST THE JOLLY ROGER AND READY THE PLANK!

HERE.

WHAT'S THIS?

OUR BOOTY!

HEY, MOM, DID YOU KNOW THAT GRAVITY IN OUTER SPACE WORKS AS IF SPACE WAS A SOFT, FLAT SURFACE? IT'S TRUE.

HEAVY MATTER, LIKE PLANETS, SINKS INTO THE SURFACE AND ANYTHING PASSING BY, LIKE LIGHT, WILL "ROLL" TOWARD THE DIP IN SPACE MADE BY THE PLANET. LIGHT IS ACTUALLY DEFLECTED BY GRAVITY! AMAZING, HUH?

AND SPEAKING OF GRAVITY, I DROPPED A PITCHER OF LEMONADE ON THE KITCHEN FLOOR WHEN MY ROLLER SKATES SLIPPED.

HOW CAN KIDS KNOW SO MUCH AND STILL BE SO DUMB?

YOU KNOW, THE WORLD SHOULD'VE BEEN DESIGNED SO EVERYONE DIDN'T HAVE TO EAT EACH OTHER TO SURVIVE. THERE SHOULD JUST BE FEWER PEOPLE AND ANIMALS TO BEGIN WITH.

AND THE WORLD CERTAINLY COULD'VE USED A MORE EVEN DISTRIBUTION OF ITS RESOURCES, THAT'S FOR SURE.

I WONDER WHY NOBODY CONSULTED YOU.

INCREDIBLE, ISN'T IT?

 I PERFORMED A SCIENTIFIC EXPERIMENT TODAY.

 YOU KNOW HOW MAPS ALWAYS SHOW NORTH AS UP AND SOUTH AS DOWN? I WANTED TO SEE IF THAT WAS TRUE OR NOT.

 WHAT DID YOU FIND OUT?

NOT MUCH. YOUR COMPASS DIDN'T SURVIVE THE TRIP SOUTH FROM THE TOP OF THE TREE.

 MY COMPASS?!

LET ME KNOW WHEN YOU GET A NEW ONE. MY JUNIOR SCIENTIST BOOK SAYS NOT TO GET DISCOURAGED BY TEMPORARY SETBACKS.

 I'VE BEEN THINKING. YOU KNOW HOW BORING DAD IS? MAYBE IT'S A BIG PHONY ACT!

 MAYBE AFTER HE PUTS US TO BED, DAD DONS SOME WEIRD COSTUME AND GOES OUT FIGHTING CRIME! MAYBE THIS WHOLE "DAD" STUFF IS JUST A SECRET IDENTITY!

 MAYBE THE MAYOR CALLS DAD ON A SECRET HOT LINE WHENEVER THE CITY'S IN TROUBLE! MAYBE DAD'S A MASKED SUPERHERO!

 IF THAT'S TRUE HE SHOULD DRIVE A COOLER CAR.

I KNOW. OURS DOESN'T EVEN HAVE A CASSETTE DECK.

 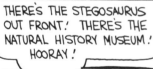 THERE'S THE STEGOSAURUS OUT FRONT! THERE'S THE NATURAL HISTORY MUSEUM! HOORAY!

 I CAN'T WAIT TO SEE ALL THE DINOSAURS! C'MON, LET'S HURRY!

 IT'S CERTAINLY BEEN A WHILE SINCE WE'VE BEEN HERE, HASN'T IT?

 AT THE MUSEUM'S REQUEST, YES.

OH, THAT'S RIGHT. CALVIN, NO BITING PEOPLE THIS TIME, REMEMBER?

RROWRR

THERE! A FULL PITCHER OF "CALVIN'S CURATIVE ELIXIR"! WE'LL CHARGE PEOPLE A BUCK A GLASS AND GET RICH!

BUT THAT'S JUST DIRTY WATER FROM THE DRAINAGE DITCH! THERE ARE LEAVES IN IT!

"FORTIFIED WITH CHLOROPHYLL," WE'LL SAY.

NOBODY'S GOING TO PAY TO DRINK THAT! ANYONE CAN SEE IT'S FILTHY! IT'S SLUDGE!

HMM... MAYBE YOU'RE RIGHT.

PITCHER OF PLAGUE
CALVIN'S DEBILITATING DISEASE DRINK!
$1.00 NOT TO HAVE ANY

WATERSON

I'VE DECIDED NOT TO GO TO SCHOOL THIS FALL.

I DON'T NEED AN EDUCATION. I DON'T NEED TO LEARN THINGS. I DON'T NEED TO DEVELOP SKILLS. IT'S TOO MUCH TROUBLE.

HOW ARE YOU GOING TO MAKE IT IN THE WORLD IF YOU DON'T KNOW ANYTHING AND YOU DON'T HAVE ANY SKILLS?!

I'LL GO ON TALK SHOWS AND HYPE MYSELF.

WATERSON

UGHH, THERE ARE TIMES WHEN I HATE OWNING A HOUSE. ALL THE MAINTENANCE!

THE WALLS NEED PAINTING, THE ROOF NEEDS TO BE FIXED, THE TREE OUT BACK NEEDS TO BE SPRAYED...

IT SEEMS LIKE THE WHOLE PLACE IS FALLING APART.

.. AND WHAT ISN'T FALLING APART IS BEING ACTIVELY DESTROYED!

CALVIN THE HUMMINGBIRD ZIPS BY WITH A LOUD WHIR!

ALTHOUGH SMALL, HE PUTS OUT TREMENDOUS ENERGY. TO HOVER, HIS WINGS BEAT HUNDREDS OF TIMES EACH SECOND!

WHAT FUELS THIS INCREDIBLE METABOLISM? CONCENTRATED SUGAR WATER! HE DRINKS HALF HIS WEIGHT A DAY!

...PREFERABLY LOADED WITH CAFFEINE.

ARE YOU DRINKING MORE SODA POP?!

"ONCE UPON A TIME THERE WAS..."

HOLD IT.

WHAT'S THE MATTER?

HAS THIS BOOK BEEN A BEST SELLER? HAS THE AUTHOR WON A PULITZER? DID THE NEW YORK TIMES LIKE IT?

I ONLY WANT STORIES THAT COME HIGHLY RECOMMENDED. ARE THERE ANY LAUDATORY QUOTES ON THE DUST JACKET?

AHEM..."ONCE UPON A TIME THERE WAS A NOISY KID WHO STARTED GOING TO BED WITHOUT A STORY."

HAS THIS BOOK BEEN MADE INTO A MOVIE? COULD WE BE WATCHING THIS ON VIDEO?

WHAT ARE YOU DOING?

I'M PRACTICING MY SNEERS.

THERE'S NOTHING LIKE A GOOD SNEER TO DRY UP CONVERSATION. HOW'S MINE LOOK?

AWFUL!

THANKS. WITH THIS SNEER, I HOPE TO BE AN UNBEARABLE BURDEN AT ANY SOCIAL OCCASION.

THAT WILL GIVE YOU A REAL HEAD START ON BEING A TEEN-AGER.

I KNOW! IT'S LIKE GETTING SEVEN EXTRA YEARS!

MOM WANTS ME TO MAKE MY BED. COME HELP ME, OK?

OK.

YOU GET SOME PENCILS, AND I'LL GET SOME BIG PAPER!

I THOUGHT WE WERE MAKING THE BED.

AND DO ALL THAT WORK?!? NO, WE'RE GOING TO INVENT A ROBOT TO MAKE THE BED *FOR* US!

WON'T INVENTING A ROBOT BE MORE WORK THAN MAKING THE BED?

IT'S ONLY WORK IF SOMEBODY MAKES YOU DO IT.

HOW ARE WE GOING TO INVENT A ROBOT? WE DON'T KNOW ANYTHING ABOUT MACHINES.

MAYBE *YOU* DON'T.

IT'S EASY. THERE ARE JUST FOUR SIMPLE MACHINES TO ALTER FORCE: THE LEVER, THE PULLEY, THE INCLINED PLANE AND, UM, THE INTERNAL COMBUSTION ENGINE.

TAKE MY WORD FOR IT, I'M AN EXPERT AT INVENTIONS.

SO WHERE DO WE START?

WE ASK MOM FOR A RESEARCH GRANT.

HI, MOM. CAN I LOOK AT YOUR WALLET FOR A FEW MINUTES? I, UH, WANT TO SEE SOMETHING.

HOLD ON. DID YOU MAKE YOUR BED LIKE I ASKED YOU?

I'M WORKING ON IT.

AS I RECALL, YOUR BED IS IN YOUR ROOM.

I'M INVENTING A ROBOT TO MAKE THE BED, BUT I NEED A GRANT. CAN I HAVE $50?

WHAT'D SHE SAY? DID YOU GET THE MONEY?

BOY, WHEN WE'RE THE COVER STORY OF POPULAR MECHANICS, I'LL HAVE SOME CHOICE WORDS TO SAY ABOUT FAMILY ENCOURAGEMENT.

THE FEARLESS SPACEMAN SPIFF IS BEING PURSUED ACROSS THE GALAXY BY DREADED SCUM BEINGS!

THEY'RE GAINING! SPIFF'S ONLY CHANCE TO LOSE THEM IS TO RELEASE A GIANT SMOKE CLOUD BEHIND HIS SPACECRAFT! OUR HERO THROWS THE LEVER!

HEH HEH... JUST UH, CLAPPING THE ERASERS, HEH HEH... (COUGH)

YOU AGAIN?

* SIGHHHH * I CAN'T BELIEVE IT'S NOT EVEN 8:30 YET.

WHAT A DAY.

I'M HO-O-AAAH!

KAPOINWW!!

THINGS GET SO DARN QUIET WHEN YOU'RE NOT AROUND.

THERE'S GOING TO BE SOME RUCKUS *NOW*, BUDDY-BOY!

IS IT? IT *IS*! IT'S **SATURDAY**! OH BOY!

NO SCHOOL! NO HOMEWORK! JUST CARTOONS AND FUN THE WHOLE DAY LONG!

HOORAY!

TURN ON THE TV! GET OUT THE CEREAL!

IT'S SAAAAT URDAY!

BONK

BONK

BONK

YOU'RE GETTING UP?? IT'S BARELY LIGHT OUT!

I'M GOING TO THE OFFICE AND GET SOME SLEEP.

Calvin and Hobbes
by WATTERSON

HMM... THE ENGINE'S MAKING FUNNY NOISES..

SPACEMAN SPIFF IS GOING DOWN OVER PLANET GORK!

ZOUNDS! THE PLANET IS INHABITED! AN ALIEN METROPOLIS OPENS UP BEFORE OUR HERO'S EYES!

SPIFF'S STABILIZERS REFUSE TO RESPOND! OUR HERO IS GOING TO CRASH!

THIS SPELLS DISASTER!

CALVIN!

"UH... D...I...S...A... S...T...E...R.

VERY GOOD. I'M GLAD YOU WERE PAYING ATTENTION.

YES! ONCE AGAIN THE INCREDIBLE SPACEMAN SPIFF BEATS ALL ODDS TO SAVE THE DAY!

YOU MAY SIT DOWN, CALVIN.

UH OH, CALVIN THE REPTILE IS IN TROUBLE!

AS AN ECTOTHERM, HIS BODY RELIES ON THE ENVIRONMENT TO WARM OR COOL ITS TEMPERATURE.

NOW THAT IT'S COLDER OUTSIDE, CALVIN'S BODY TEMPERATURE FALLS AND HE BECOMES SLUGGISH! HE'LL GO INTO TORPOR IF HE CAN'T FIND A WARM PLACE TO LIE!

LEAVE THE THERMOSTAT ALONE, AND PUT ON A SWEATER IF YOU'RE COLD.

I...I DON'T HAVE THE EN..ENERGY!

I HEARD THAT BIG CATS DON'T PURR.

THAT'S TRUE. WE'RE TOO FIERCE AND FEROCIOUS. WE DON'T EVER PURR.

WELL WHAT DO YOU CALL THE NOISE YOU MAKE WHEN YOU GET YOUR TUMMY RUBBED?!

GROWLING FRIENDLY-LIKE.

CALVIN, YOUR MOM AND I LOOKED OVER YOUR REPORT CARD, AND WE THINK YOU COULD BE DOING BETTER.

BUT I DON'T LIKE SCHOOL.

WHY NOT? YOU LIKE TO READ AND YOU LIKE TO LEARN. I KNOW YOU DO.

I MEAN, YOU'VE READ EVERY DINOSAUR BOOK EVER WRITTEN, AND YOU'VE LEARNED A LOT, RIGHT? READING AND LEARNING ARE FUN.

YEAH..

SO WHY DON'T YOU LIKE SCHOOL?

WE DON'T READ ABOUT DINOSAURS.

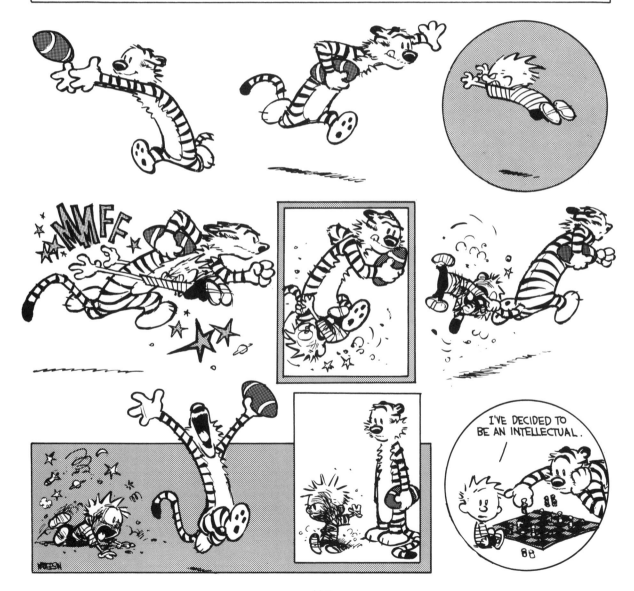

The End